Kevin's birthday was in two days.
His Mum and Dad asked him what he
wanted for his birthday.
Kevin wanted a horse.

1

'A horse?' said Mr Miller. 'What about a dog?'
'No!' said Kevin.
'What about a cat?' said his mother.
'No!' said Kevin.

2

'What about a canary?' said Mr Miller.
'No. I want a horse!' said Kevin.
'We will talk about this later,' said Mr Miller.

Later that day Kevin and his Dad went out.
They went out to see some friends of
Mr Miller.
Kevin still wanted to talk about a horse.

'We have a horse,' said the men.
'Can I see him?' asked Kevin.
'You can see him,' said the men, 'but he is too quick for you.'

Kevin looked at the horse.
The horse looked at Kevin.
'He is not too quick for me,' said Kevin.

Kevin grabbed the horse and jumped up.
'No!' shouted the men.
'Get down, Kevin!' shouted his Dad.

Kevin was too quick.
The horse ran off with him.
Mr Miller and the men followed.

The horse ran over the grass.

It ran up to a fence.
It jumped the fence.

It ran up to a wall.
The wall was higher than the fence.
The horse stopped but...

Kevin could not!

He went over the wall.
He splashed into some water.

Mr Miller and the men ran up to Kevin.
'Are you hurt?' asked his Dad.
'No,' said Kevin. 'I am not hurt.'

Good,' said Mr Miller.
Do you still want a horse?' he asked.
No,' said Kevin. 'I do not want a horse now.'
You could still make friends with the horse,'
said Mr Miller.

Kevin gave the horse some apples and they
made friends.